MW00788149

SUPER AGENTS
SAFETY SQUAD

By: Denize Rodrigues

Elani PUBLISHING

Super Agent Safety Squad

Copyright © 2019 by Denize Rodrigues

All Rights Reserved.

No part of this book may be reproduced in any form or by any electronic or mechanical means, including information storage and retrieval systems, without written permission, except in the case of a reviewer who may quote brief passages embodied in critical articles or in a review.

If you would like to do any of the above or purchase individual or bulk copies, please contact:

www.SASSkids.com

Printed in the United States.

ISBN: 978-0-578-58827-8

While we have attempted to provide up-to-date and correct information, there are no representations or warranties, express or implied, about the completeness, accuracy, reliability, suitability, or availability with respect to the information contained within.

Book development editor, cover/interior design, and promotion: S.A. Jernigan, Renaissance Consultations (www.MarketingAndPR.com)

Original illustrations designed by Aneeza Ashraf

Cover Design + Updated Layout by Peter Mitchell

DEDICATION

This book is dedicated to my niece Emily Silva. I thank God for you and the joy you have brought to our lives.

FOREWORD

The intrusive violation of childhood sexual abuse is an attack on a child's personhood. It is estimated that 1 out of every 10 (1 out of 5 girls, 1 out of 20 boys) children will be victimized before their 8th birthday and that number is the one provided while also reporting that 60% of victims never tell.

As an expert and a survivor in the area of childhood trauma, I know and understand the devastating and debilitating impact it can have on every part of a person's life – emotional, behavioral, physical, psychological, cognitively, economically – its reach is unbiased and irreverent.

In this book, Super Agents Safety Squad, Denize Rodrigues' easy-to-understand presentation equips parents, caregivers, and children with the empowerment and confidence needed to prevent and reduce risk factors concerning this life altering phenomenon. Denize is asking us to pull away from our distractions of life and take some time to increase our awareness to this brutality and the defenselessness of the young lives it impacts. The message is simple, but profound; small, but, oh so, powerful.

If you are in a position to influence the life of a child for the good, I am inviting you to join me to partner with Denize and become a member of the Super Agents Safety Squad.

Dr. Ivy Bonk is the principal of Every Child Whole, LLC. She possesses a doctorate in Educational Psychology with a research focus in the area of childhood trauma and its impact on learning and development with a certification in the Neurosequential Modeling in Education (NME) from The Neurosequential Network (Child Trauma Academy/Dr. Bruce Perry). She is also the author of The Day Trauma Came to Class and Lost: Finding my way Back to a Place I've Never Been.

INTRODUCTION

By way of introduction, I am the mom of two wonderful kids: Jennifer's 11 and Davi is 7. My husband and I are both immigrants from Brazil and have made our home in Northern California for 12 years now. We have a busy life with our two kids, and family activities; we also run our own business.

Both sides of our families still live in Brazil. In 2016, I had the privilege of bringing my niece here for a visit; she was 14 at the time. Our family was very excited awaiting her arrival. After attending a church youth meeting one day, she confided to me in tears that she was abused in the past and had never told anyone because, after trying a few times, she feared no one would believe her. Upon hearing this horrific news, I was in shock and felt disgusted and so angry especially when I learned the offender was a close family relative of hers.

I immediately started consulting friends who are lawyers and judges in Brazil to learn how we might have him prosecuted for this crime. They all responded that it would only be possible if my niece returned to Brazil. After spending a long period of time in prayer and going back and forth with all the scenarios and in the aftermath of receiving threats from other members of the offender's family we decided the risks in returning her to Brazil would just be too great.

I know that God will have His justice done in this matter, but now we are invested in helping her rebuild her life and guiding her in the right direction, knowing that God has a great plan for my niece here in the U.S.

Not long after her confession, she approached me and asked what I was doing to teach and warn my own kids so they would know what to do if something like this ever happened to them. Once again, I was floored and just knew in my heart in that moment I MUST do something in response to her question.

The way my husband and I are raising our kids always focuses on empowering them by giving them tools for life. But I confess that this subject had never crossed my mind, and I simply wasn't ready for it. Perhaps it's because it's such a dark and disturbing type of assault on the most vulnerable among us...children.

So, I went ahead and started to research, including buying all the kids books I could find that might touch on this topic. That's when the idea for this book came to me. With my niece's help, while thinking carefully about what language would work with my own youngsters, and after many sleepless nights asking God what was on His heart in this matter, "Super Agents - Safety Squad" was born.

My goal with this book is to educate and empower parents with tools to talk about a subject so important, and yet so often left unspoken... until something close to home happens. Or, worse yet, something unexpected inside our own home happens...and most of the time it's too late by then. With my niece, her perpetrator was someone whom her family trusted, an uncle who sometimes would babysit her while her parents were at work as they were also neighbors.

According to child sexual abuse articles on www.Rainn.org, the majority of perpetrators are someone the child or family knows. As many as 93% of victims under the age of 18 know their abuser. And I would like to state the obvious, namely that the perpetrator will not make their move under our watchful eye!

WHAT IS CHILD ABUSE?

Child sexual abuse is a form of child abuse that includes any sexual activity with a minor. A child cannot consent to any form of sexual activity, period. When a perpetrator engages with a child in this way, they are committing a crime which can also have lasting effects on the victim for years. Child sexual abuse does not need to include physical contact between a perpetrator and a child.

Some forms of child sexual abuse include:

- Exhibitionism, or exposing oneself to a minor
- Fondling
- Obscene phone calls, text messages, or digital interaction
- Producing, owning, or sharing pornographic images or videos of children
- Masturbation in the presence of a minor, or forcing the minor to masturbate
- Sex of any kind with a minor, including vaginal, oral, or anal
- Sex trafficking
- Intercourse
- Any other sexual conduct that is harmful to a child's mental, emotional, or physical welfare.

Our kids need to know what is the right and healthy behavior between them and the adults in their lives and when a red line is crossed. Parents, we need to be aware that, unfortunately, this aberrant behavior happens more often than we think, and is typically perpetrated by somebody close, so we often "never see it coming."

In this book, I've compiled some research and put together some practical tips as well as signs to be watching for in your day-to-day life for both you and your kids. *Super Agents - Safety Squad is intended to be read by parents and kids TOGETHER.* Please make this a special time to open up a conversation on this sensitive topic and bond with your child.

As parents, we often want to raise our kids in a protective bubble, shielded from any and all harm, but unfortunately this is not how life plays out in the real world. So, it's a key part of our parental duty that WE PREPARE THEM for any situation so that, hopefully, when they're out there in the world, they will be equipped with the knowledge necessary and know how to respond in a way that will protect them. However, if you are reading this book because you already have concerns about the welfare of your child or someone you know, please pay close attention to this next section.

DON'T BE CLUELESS...

This subject is broad so I surely can't cover it comprehensively here. But I will give you this online resource where you can obtain more information needed to address various child sexual abuse scenarios (plus see the Parent Resources section in the book's conclusion). According to this article (www.AnxiousToddlers.com/signs-of-sexual-abuse), child therapist Natasha Daniels, LCSW, provides important tips for parents to watch out for. Because I thought everything she says here is of vital importance, I reached out and obtained her permission to share this information of hers here with you (as follows):

You have concerns. You have suspicions. But, how can you be sure? You want that definitive list. Those definitive signs and behaviors to confirm or disconfirm your worst beliefs about sexual abuse.

Unfortunately, no one can do that for you – not even this article. Sexual abuse isn't like a disease, with its obvious checklist of symptoms. Kids respond and react differently to child sexual abuse; therefore no one can definitively tell you that your suspicions are right or wrong.

What I can tell you, however, are behaviors that warrant concern. There are some behaviors, which as a child therapist, make me take a closer look.

Having said that, I need to make one point abundantly clear. Many children do not show any signs of child sexual abuse. Many of the children I see in my practice never gave any indication of sexual abuse prior to it being discovered.

Here are signs that would make a therapist concerned. Please note – these behaviors aren't necessarily an indicator of sexual abuse, but are concerning behaviors nonetheless. If you are concerned that your child might be a victim of sexual abuse, please take them to a child therapist to be evaluated as soon as possible. If you know a child that is being sexually abused, you need to report it to law enforcement.

Behaviors that are concerning:

Sexualized Play

If your very young child is having sexualized play with their dolls or toys, this is concerning behavior. It isn't abnormal for children to have their dolls kissing or laying on top of each other, but it would be atypical for a child to be acting out oral sex or other sexualized acts with their toys.

Penetrating Themselves with Objects

This may be hard to talk about, but if young children are taking toys or fingers and sticking them up their anus or vagina, this warrants concern. Children will explore their body parts, but it is less common for children to digitally penetrate themselves with objects or fingers.

Inappropriately Touching Others

If your child is trying to touch adults or children in their private areas, this can be a concern. Children are curious and will explore with each other, but if your child is putting their mouth on another child's private parts or is digitally penetrating other kids – this goes beyond exploration.

Bleeding and Infection from Private Parts

If your child has bleeding, infection or bruising around or in their private area for unknown reasons, this is a concern. Get them to the doctor right away for a full exam.

Playing Secret Sexualized Games

If children are wanting to play secret body games with their friends, this deserves further exploration. Many children will play games that involve private parts as part of normal exploration and development, but If kids have a name for the game and special nicknames for various private parts, this might be more than typical play. Often pedophiles will incorporate games and special nicknames for private parts to manipulate children. Sexually abused kids will often attempt to play these games with other kids around them.

A Strong Negative Response Around a Particular Person

If your child is normally polite, but they are uncharacteristically rude or frightened by a person they encounter, it would be worth exploring further. It is important to note, that many of the children I have worked with continued to be friendly or affectionate to the person that was sexually abusing them. This was often the reason parents dismissed any of their concerns or gut feelings. Do not discount abuse just because your child does not show signs of anger or fear around a person you have concerns about.

The US Department of Justice's National Sex Offender Public Website (NSOPW) lists 12 other behaviors that can be signs of possible sexual abuse.

As a child therapist, I know that many of these behaviors are very general and can be caused by other issues as well, therefore it is important to seek out the guidance of a professional for a full assessment.

- *Has nightmares or other sleep problems without an explanation. Seems distracted or distant at odd times*
- *Has a sudden change in eating habits*
- *Refuses to eat*
- *Loses or drastically increases appetite*
- *Has trouble swallowing*

- *Sudden mood swings: rage, fear, insecurity, or withdrawal*
- *Leaves "clues" that seem likely to provoke a discussion about sexual issues*
- *Develops new or unusual fear of certain people or places*
- *Refuses to talk about a secret shared with an adult or older child*
- *Writes, draws, plays, or dreams of sexual or frightening images*
- *Talks about a new older friend*

If you are seeing any of the above warning signs, or if you just have that parental gut feeling – talk to a professional. These signs may not point directly to sexual abuse, but they do indicate there is a problem in general that needs exploring.

For more information on how to detect sexual abuse visit:

www.ParentsProtect.co.uk/warning_signs.htm (very thorough article on this topic)
*www.StopItNow.org/ohc-content/tip-sheet-7 *

My thanks to Ms. Daniels for providing this invaluable information of hers. Let me say in closing, from my family to yours, I truly hope this book will help you and your own children gain awareness so as to keep them safe and protected, and hopefully you will also share these words of prevention with others. A wise motto you've probably heard is a guiding and practical one: "Always hope for the best but be prepared for the worst."

May God bless you & your children,

Denise
Rodriguez

Acknowledgements

I would like to thank my Lord and Savior Jesus Christ.
Much thanks to my family – my husband, Luciano Lima and our kids,
Jennifer Lima and Davi Lima. Thanks to all the professionals who assisted in
making this book a reality.

Hi everyone, my name is Tony, and this is my sister, Lily. We just received our badge from the **SAFETY SQUAD!**

Now we're part of their **SUPER AGENTS TEAM**, and our job is to make sure kids around us are safe and protected, including ourselves.

WHAT ABOUT YOU?

Would **YOU** like to **JOIN US** on this **MISSION** of ours?

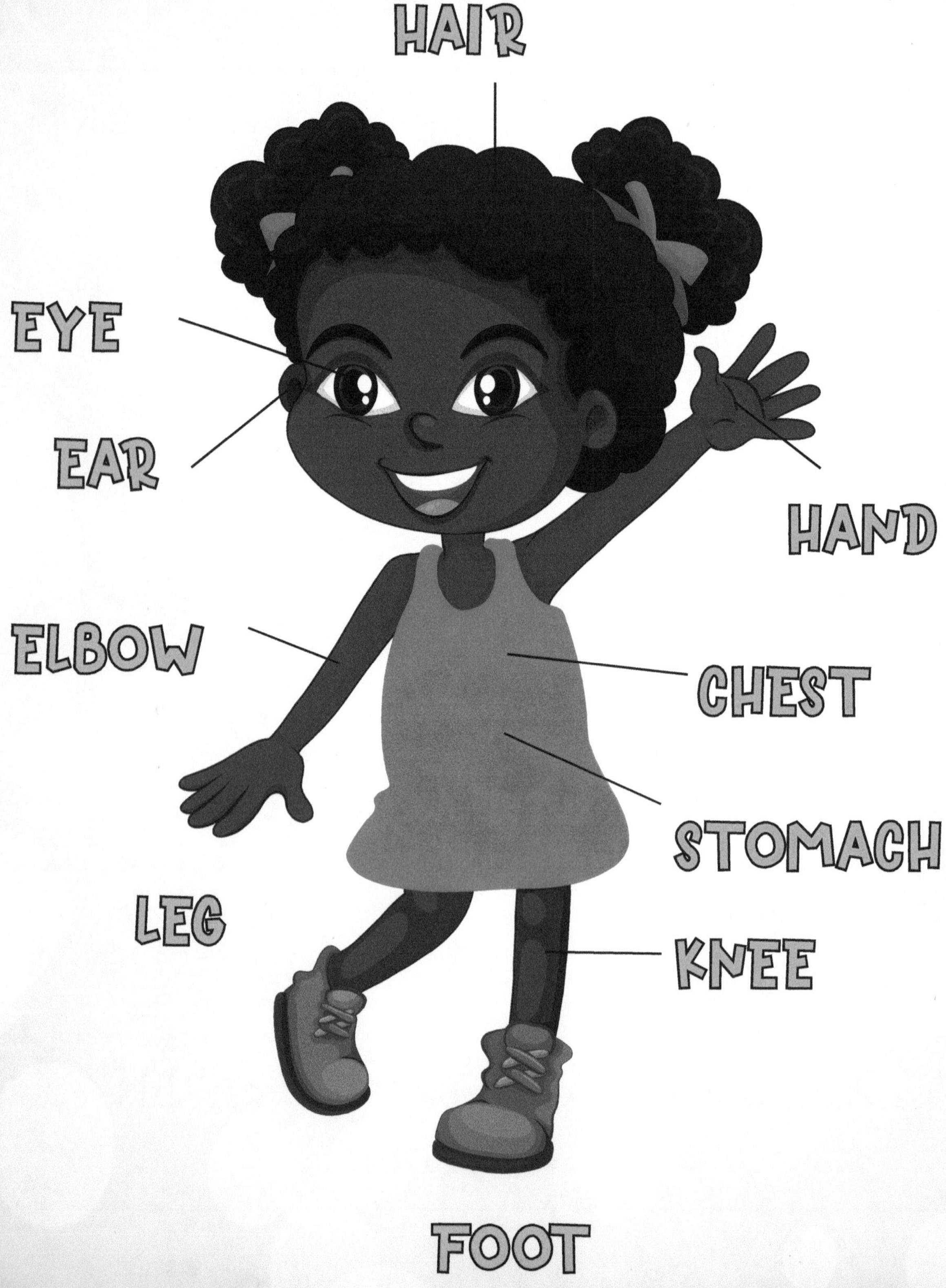

HAIR

EYE

EAR

ELBOW

LEG

HAND

CHEST

STOMACH

KNEE

FOOT

Let's start talking about our bodies. We have eyes, hair, ears, legs, and arms. We call these our body parts. Each one carries out specific functions necessary for everyday life. Some parts are okay to be seen by other people, like our hair, hands, and legs. BUT THERE ARE OTHER BODY PARTS...

Tony started to jump up and down saying,

"I KNOW, I KNOW! THERE ARE OTHER PARTS OF YOUR BODY WE CALL "PRIVATE PARTS."

DO YOU KNOW WHAT THAT MEANS?

It means they belong ONLY TO YOU, so only YOU are allowed to see, and touch. You are also responsible to keep these parts clean and safe!

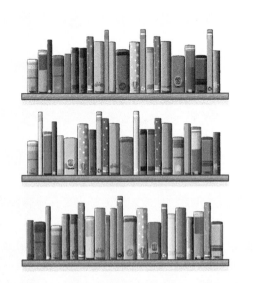

Today, we will share **IMPORTANT RULES** that will help keep you safe and sound.

Let's introduce you to our teacher who will help us give you the best training possible, ok?

Her name is **MRS. GRACE.**

"Mrs. Grace, will you please explain to our friends WHICH PARTS OF OUR BODIES ARE OUR PRIVATE PARTS?" asked Lily.

"Of course, Lily."

(THIS IS IMPORTANT, CHILDREN...!)

For girls, private parts are the ones **COVERED BY A BIKINI.**

For boys, private parts are **COVERED BY UNDERWEAR.**

PARENT NOTE: at this point, please comment on their private parts. If you use different names for these parts, please bring them up now so you're equipped to have a conversation on this topic.

Lily then began saying that when she was between two and four years old she had to be potty-trained, and her parents needed to help her out because she was too little to clean up.

Then Mrs. Grace went on to say

THERE ARE TIMES WHEN A FEW PEOPLE ARE ALLOWED TO HELP YOU OUT IN THESE SORTS OF SPECIAL SITUATIONS, and that's just fine!

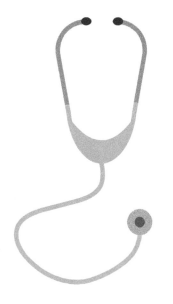

Mrs. Grace then continued, "When you get sick and need to go to the doctor with Mom and Dad, or any other adult you trust, the doctor might need to see your private parts just to check that everything's okay.

THAT'S ALSO FINE.

PARENT NOTE: You might share with your child a LIST of people who would be allowed to do so.

"Have you seen a **TRAFFIC LIGHT?** How many colors are there?" asked Mrs. Grace.

"I know, I know!" answered Lily, trying to contain her excitement.

Three:

RED

YELLOW

& GREEN

"What do they mean?" **ASKED MRS. GRACE.**

Then it was Tony's turn to answer.

 "The color GREEN means you are FREE TO GO!

             means   , it's about to get

 And **RED** means **STOP NOW!**

"Excellent, Tony!" said Mrs. Grace.

As the traffic light has these color codes which help us know what to do in any situation, we will also use these same color codes to help us on our **SUPER MISSION** as **SUPER AGENTS** with **SAFETY SQUAD.**

 **SAFETY TIP**

Now we will play a game and you will tell me what color this situation represents, ok? Ready?

READY!

Here's our first example. Your BABYSITTER needs to help you CHANGE to go to the park.

Next, your GRANDPARENTS just arrived for a visit and they give you lots of HUGS and KISSES.

Or, YOU and your FRIENDS are celebrating your favorite team's victory by HUGGING and HIGH-FIVES.

You guys are so smart! I can see you REALLY want to earn that super special badge!

LET'S SEE IF YOU CAN HELP WITH THIS NEXT SITUATION...

SAFETY SQUAD

You are going to a   with your
          , but she loves to
          and always asks you to   things from
her   . Lily gasped, perplexed,

"Yes, Lily," said Mrs. Grace.

BE CAREFUL!

"You will need to be careful. If you can't tell an adult what you are about to do, hear, or watch, that also means you will not have their protection if needed!

Therefore,

If an   you know or a   wants to be with you and always invites you to be with them when

Tony said,

When someone gives you a candy or a gift and asks you to NOT tell anyone in exchange for a secret.

Tony replied, "WE SHOULD NOT KEEP SECRETS FROM THE PEOPLE WHO LOVE US!"

What if your brother, one of his friends, an uncle, aunt, grandma, or grandpa, someone you know OR anybody else asks to SEE or TOUCH your private parts when nobody is around?

Tony said loudly, "Red, Red, RED! STOP SIGN!"

Then he ran around the room pretending to be a police car, "wheeeow... !" and making a noise like a siren.

Then everybody laughed, and Mrs. Grace said, "That's right, Tony! RED FOR STOP!"

NOW HERE'S THE MOST IMPORTANT PART OF OUR MISSION!

It is super important you join SAFETY SQUAD AS A SUPER AGENT and help us expose people who are hiding and pretending to be good, kind, and caring people.

They could be big kids, teenagers, or grownups. When they are around other people, they pretend to be like everybody else...
happy, nice, and caring.

But when they are alone with kids, they start to tell them lies, trying to get them to do things that are NOT NICE OR SAFE.

DO YOU KNOW WHAT ELSE THEY MAY SAY?

"IF YOU KEEP THIS SECRET, I WILL GIVE YOU A NEW TOY"...or..."IF YOU DON'T TELL, I WILL BRING YOU TO THE PARK,"...or..."I WILL BE YOUR BEST FRIEND FOREVER AND THIS IS JUST OUR PRIVATE GAME."

Sometimes they might even **THREATEN** you or your family saying, "**IF YOU TELL ANYONE, I WILL HURT YOUR SISTER OR YOUR MOM!**"

Then Tony scratched his head, feeling very confused.

"**BUT...MRS. GRACE, WHAT SHOULD I DO IF THAT HAPPENS?**"

"Good question, Tony," said Mrs. Grace.

They don't want **YOU** to tell anyone because **THEY** are actually **VERY SCARED!**

They know that what they're asking of you is very WRONG... and if you keep it a SECRET they will be able to keep doing it! DO NOT BELIEVE THEM! IT'S A LIE!!

SAFETY TIP

Look around and find someone you trust that you can run too!

Tell your Mom, Dad, or another grown-up you trust—When you tell on them,

IT ALL STOPS!

"What if my friends ask me to show them my **PRIVATE PARTS** or they want to show me **THEIRS**, does that count as **A RED LIGHT?**" asked Lily.

ABSOLUTELY!!! THEY WOULD BE VIOLATING YOUR PRIVACY!

THIS WOULD BE A BIG RED LIGHT!

"What if I'm in the school's bathroom and a big kid wants to touch or see my private parts, or even wants to show me somebody else's in a magazine, or on their phone?

THAT'S A RED LIGHT, RIGHT?" asked Tony, sounding very concerned.

"RED LIGHT, RED SIGN, AND RED SIREN," answered Mrs. Grace.

If anyone tries to tell you this is normal, say it out loud, "THIS IS NOT NORMAL!" And then GET OUT of there immediately!

Find someone you trust and TELL! Telling someone you trust will also make you feel better!

SAFETY TIP

 You will have now COMPLETED YOUR MISSION as a Super Agent with SAFETY SQUAD!

If you're reading this book at your school, your church, or at a friend's house, and for any reason you don't feel safe telling your parents about a problem like this, please find a teacher, an aunt, or a neighbor you trust and

TELL, TELL, TELL!

We want you to know that YOU ARE NOT ALONE! If something like this has already happened to you, there are many kids this has happened to in the past, and some are still living with a similar situation.

We want you to know no matter what, where, when, or **WHO** is doing this, you can **ALWAYS** say,

"STOP! THAT'S ENOUGH!"

And know it's also **NOT YOUR FAULT!**

Find someone you trust and ask for help! Then Lily and Tony thanked Mrs. Grace for all her help.

Lily said,

"The Super Agents from **SAFETY SQUAD** want to help all us kids feel protected, safe, and smart about what to DO if these kind of situations ever happen.

That's why we are super excited to have YOU helping us on this VERY important mission!

As a **SUPER AGENT** from **SAFETY SQUAD**, you now know if you keep this kind of secret, they will just keep doing it to you... and ALSO to other kids around them. When you do the right thing, you protect yourself

—and other kids as well!

CONGRATULATIONS!! You have now completed this Super Class with the Safety Squad! And you've earned your "Super Agent" I.D. card (at the end of the book) so you'll always **BE READY** to keep yourself and other kids **SAFE**.

Show your parents whenever you have any GREEN, , or RED-LIGHT situations and TALK to them about it!

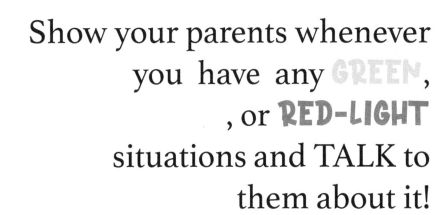

See you next time, SUPER-AGENT.

Thank you for joining us on our important mission & STAY SAFE!

PARENT RESOURCES

Support on the Web:
www.PreventChildAbuse.org

www.d2l.org

www.rainn.org

www.nsvrc.org

And
visit **SUPER AGENTS
SAFETY SQUAD**
online for additional
information and helpful
tips: SASSkids.com

REPORTING NUMBERS IN YOUR STATE

Hotlines

Prevent Child Abuse America: (800) CHILDREN

Circle of Parents: (773) 257-0111×3

Grandparent Information Center: (800) 424-3410

Let's **ALL** join **TOGETHER**
and help keep **KIDS** **S-A-F-E**
AND JUST HAPPY BEING KIDS...!

SUPER AGENT I.D. CARD INSTRUCTIONS

Parents, please assist your children as needed in carefully cutting this next page from the book:

OK, kids, here's your **SUPER AGENT SAFETY SQUAD** I.D. card — you've earned it! Pease have your parents help you carefully cut this out, and then carry your Super Agent I.D. card with you in your pocket, wallet, purse, or backpack so you will always keep yourself & other kids **SAFE!**

- **Fold in half**
- **Use tape or glue to fasten the two sides in place**
- **Optional: for a sturdier card, remove its backing and place onto contact paper, OR glue onto lightweight cardboard, and trim**

We appreciate your partnership in equipping your kid(s) with this card in order to keep our red, yellow, green lessons and tell, Tell, TELL instructions from the **SAFETY SQUAD** handy for them **Thank You!**

LEARN more & additional I.D. cards available:
www.sasskids.com

OK, kids, here's your SUPER AGENT SAFETY SQUAD I.D. card — you've earned it! Pease have your parents help you carefully cut this out, and then carry your Super Agent I.D. card with you in your pocket, wallet, purse, or backpack so you will always keep yourself & other kids SAFE!

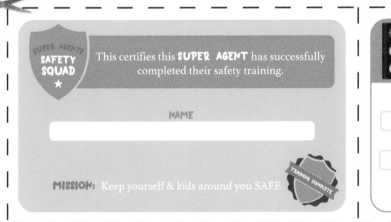

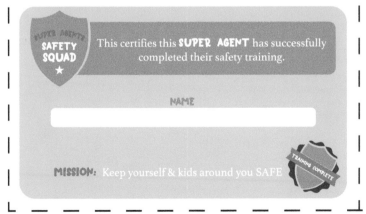

Now that you've completed your mission here's your SUPER AGENT SAFETY SQUAD badge. All you have to do is cut out your favorite color!

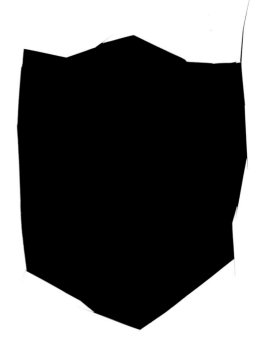

Can you help me find the **BODY PARTS** that others can see?

```
        K I L J R R F X
      G M M Z O D J R X A O C
    H A I R K F H A N D S C V W
    G B N A   R Y E M     D A G Q
    A T T H K   W H U B     W R O O U
    I K T F N   Y Z T N     S M E B Z
    L E G S I K   O O U A   D S A S C O
    T M X E N A   D Y U X   T R R Y L U
    V B R G G T   R C U J   K E S Y K D
    U C L P E E Z N P V Y B D O N J E Y L K
    J Y F L R K C R G M S U H J E N G F L E
    F K F G S N T E O E Q B V C D J Y A Z T
    B G O   T O E S Y L V M A N E E   P K U
    Y K H   H S E U Q D F D B N     G X Y
    E E S   O M S Z F C L R     O D H
    G Y L U               R K D C
    T L B P             X G O C
    V U O F K N E E S A W Q Q G
    Z D W H U F T I B O O T
    F F S L H R R D
```

WORD LIST

Arms	Eyes	Fingers	Knees
Ears	Face	Hair	Legs
Elbow	Feet	Hands	Toes

Can you help Lily solve the puzzle?

Across

3 Find someone you trust and _____!

4 For boys, private parts are COVERED BY _____.

7 THERE ARE OTHER PARTS OF YOUR BODY WE CALL "_____."

8 "The color_____means you are FREE TO GO!

9 For girls, private parts are the ones COVERED BY A _____.

10 And RED means_____ NOW!

Down

1 YELLOW means CAUTION, it's about to get RISKY ' PAY _____!

2 It means they belong ONLY TO ____.

5 You will have now COMPLETED YOUR _____.

6 WE SHOULD NOT KEEP_____FROM THE PEOPLE WHO LOVE US!

ANSWERS

Game 1

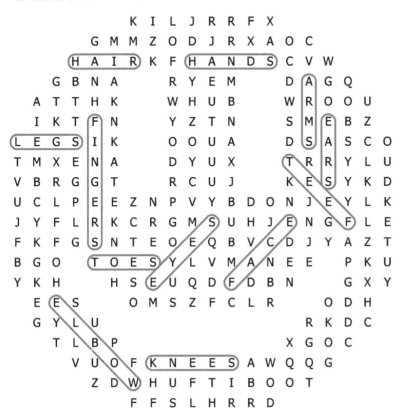

```
        K I L J R R F X
      G M M Z O D J R X A O C
    (H A I R) K F (H A N D S) C V W
    G B N A       R Y E M    D A G Q
  A T T H K       W H U B    W R O O U
  I K T F N       Y Z T N    S M E B Z
 (L E G S) I K    O O U A    D S A S C O
  T M X E N A     D Y U X    T R R Y L U
  V B R G G T     R C U J    K E S Y K D
  U C L P E E Z N P V Y B D O N J E Y L K
  J Y F L R K C R G M S U H J E N G F L E
  F K F G S N T E O E Q B V C D J Y A Z T
  B G O (T O E S) Y L V M A N E E   P K U
  Y K H     H S E U Q D F D B N     G X Y
    E E S       O M S Z F C L R     O D H
    G Y L U               R K D C
    T L B P               X G O C
    V U O F (K N E E S) A W Q Q G
      Z D W H U F T I B O O T
      F F S L H R R D
```

Game 2

Across	Down
3. Tell	1. Attention
4. Underwear	2. You
7. Privateparts	5. Mission
8. Green	6. Secrets
9. Bikini	
10. Stop	

MY ART SPACE

MY ART SPACE

CPSIA information can be obtained
at www.ICGtesting.com
Printed in the USA
JSHW011656071219
2858JS00002B/4

9 780578 588278